ALPHABET
Sticker Activity Book
100 WORDS

Have fun completing this sticker activity book.

Use your pens and pencils to colour
the pictures. Where there is a missing sticker,
you will see an empty shape. Search your
sticker pages to find the missing sticker.

Then, press out the cards at the back of the
book and use them to play a game!

make believe ideas

A a

alligator

aeroplane

ambulance

astronaut

Which fruit begins with a?

ant

apple

arrow

B b

banana

bear

bird

boat

Point to the vehicles.

C c

cupcake

clock

car

cloud

Dd

digger

dog

drum

duck

Find the musical instrument.

Ee

engine

egg

envelope

elephant

F f

frog

Can you point to the fish's fins?

flamingo

fan

fin

fish

flower

fence

5

G g goat

What do you wear on your head?

grapes

gift

guitar

H h

heart

hat

house

hoof horse

I i

iguana

igloo

insect

ice cream

J j

jewel

jacket

Find the ice-cold treat.

jar

jellyfish

K k

kite

key

Meow! kitten

koala

What sound does a kitten make?

L l

lion

lamp

leaf

lemon

M m

moon

map

milk

monkey — mouth

How many animals can you see?

motorbike

mountain

mouse

mask

mug

N n

nest

net

nut

nine

O o

octopus

orange

otter

Colour the bird in the nest.

owl

P

peach

penguin

parrot

piano

Point to the things you can eat.

Q

quail

quilt

quiche

queen

R r

rocket

What flies in space?

ring

radio

rhinoceros

S s

snake

star

scarf

strawberry

T t

toy train

toothbrush

tent

tomato

Where is the toy?

tyre → truck

tractor

tree

U u

unicorn

ukulele

umbrella

Point to the blue things.

volcano

V v

vet

vase

van

14

W w

window

wolf

watch

wasp

Which object tells the time?

X x

xylophone

box

fox

Y y

yak

yo-yo

yacht

yoghurt

Find the stripy animal.

Z z

zero

zip

zebra

PAIRS AND MATCH

Pairs (one or more players)

1) Press out the cards, and put them picture-side down on a table.
2) Take turns turning over two cards. If the cards match, put them to one side. If they do not match, return them picture-side down to the table.
3) Keep going until you have found all the pairs. The player with the most pairs at the end is the winner!

Match (two or more players)

1) Divide the cards equally between the players, picture-side down.
2) Take turns turning over a card and putting it on a pile in the middle of the table, picture-side up.
3) If a card matches the card beneath it, players call out, "Match!" The first player to call out takes all the cards on the pile.
4) When players have no cards left, they are out of the game. The last player left holding cards is the winner.

bird	bird	dog	dog
lemon	lemon	apple	apple
tomato	tomato	jellyfish	jellyfish

Stickers for pages 2-3

Pages 4-5

Pages 6-7

Pages 8-9